Health 4

A Healthy You

Student Workbook

Alpha Omega Publications, Inc. • Rock Rapids, IA

Horizons Health 4 Student Workbook

© MMVII by Alpha Omega Publications, Inc.
804 N. 2nd Ave. E., Rock Rapids, IA 51246-1759
All rights reserved.

The materials within this book are protected by the copyright laws of the United States. No part of this publication may be reproduced, stored in an electronic retrieval system, or transmitted in any form by any means—electronic, mechanical, photocopy, recording or otherwise—without the prior written permission of Alpha Omega Publications, Inc. Brief quotations may be used in literary review.

CHRISTIAN SCHOOLS INTERNATIONAL

The framework for this curriculum was provided by:
CHRISTIAN SCHOOLS INTERNATIONAL
3350 East Paris Ave. SE
Grand Rapids, Michigan 49512-3054

Printed in the United States of America

ISBN 978-0-7403-1509-1

God Knows Who I Am

Look up the Bible verses (NIV) to fill in the blanks or use the words in the word bank to complete the crossword puzzle. (Hint: Count the number of letters in each word. Start with the longest words.)

Word Bank

become	guard	rescue	saints	searched	sinful	understand
birth	know	righteousness		sin	thanks	want

Psalm 139:1: "O LORD, you have _____ me and you _____ me."

Psalm 51:5: "Surely, I was _____ at _____ ."

Romans 7:15: "I do not _____ what I do. For what I _____ to do I do not do, but what I hate I do."

Romans 7:24–25a: "Who will _____ me from this body of death? _____ be to God...through Jesus Christ our Lord."

2 Corinthians 5:21: "God made him who had no _____ to be sin for us, so that in him we might _____ the _____ of God."

1 Samuel 2:9: "He will _____ the feet of his _____ ."

Feelings Cube

Cut along solid lines and fold on dotted lines to form a cube. Glue or tape the cube together.

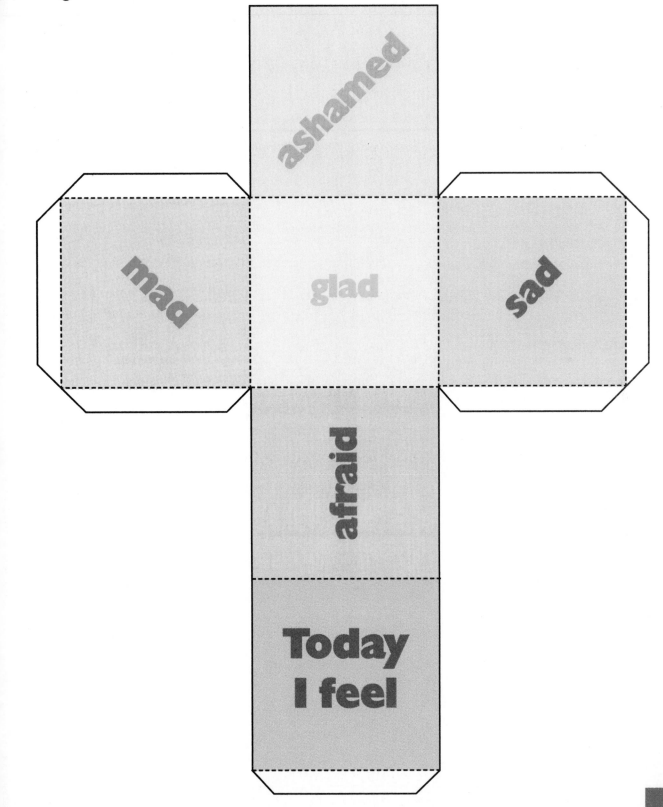

My Feelings

Here are a few sentences telling about a time I felt...

• scared

_____

_____

_____

• angry

_____

_____

_____

• sad

_____

_____

_____

• jealous

_____

_____

_____

This story is about one of the happiest days of my life.

_____

_____

_____

_____

_____

_____

_____

_____

_____

Think Again!

Change the put-downs to boosters.

Put-downs	Boosters
1. Everyone is better at baseball than I am. I'll never be any good at it.	1. _____ _____ _____
2. I'm so stupid. I'll never understand this math.	2. _____ _____ _____
3. I feel so ugly with these new glasses. My friends will all make fun of me.	3. _____ _____ _____
4. I'm always the last to be picked. I'm a loser.	4. _____ _____ _____
5. I'm not going to try out for the team. I'll never make it anyway.	5. _____ _____ _____

Tell about a time you put yourself down. Change your put-down to a booster.

_____

_____

_____

_____

_____

_____

_____

What Would You Decide?

Read each cartoon. What decision would you make? Follow the steps for making decisions. Keep God's tests in mind. Then fill in the empty word balloon. Be ready to explain why you made the decision.

Draw your own cartoon. Show a situation that needs a decision. Write the dialogue in word balloons above each person's head.

Being Me

1. **Stop and think about some of the things you have learned about yourself during this unit. Then complete the following "I learned" sentences. Each one should tell a different thing you have learned about yourself.**

   - I learned _____

   _____

   - I learned _____

   _____

   - I learned _____

   _____

2. **Please answer the following questions. Use complete sentences.**

   - What can you say and do to show others that you appreciate them?

   _____

   _____

   _____

   - What is one way to get over angry feelings?

   _____

   _____

   - List the steps to follow in making a decision.

   _____

   _____

   _____

   _____

   - What tests did God give us to help us make good decisions?

   _____

   _____

   _____

What I Look Like

Pair up with another student and look for the following characteristics in each other. Then circle the characteristic you see in yourself. Some characteristics are dominant (D); others are recessive (R).

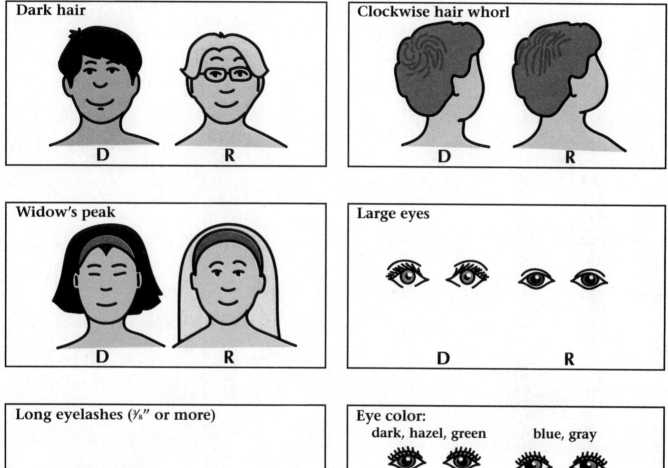

Dark hair
D   R

Clockwise hair whorl
D   R

Widow's peak
D   R

Large eyes
D   R

Long eyelashes (⅜" or more)

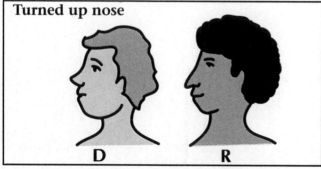

D   R

Eye color:
dark, hazel, green   blue, gray

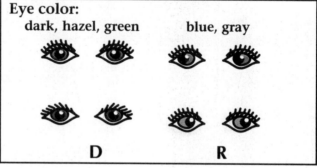

D   R

Turned up nose

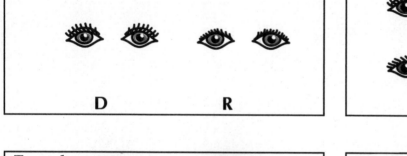

D   R

Dimples

D   R

17

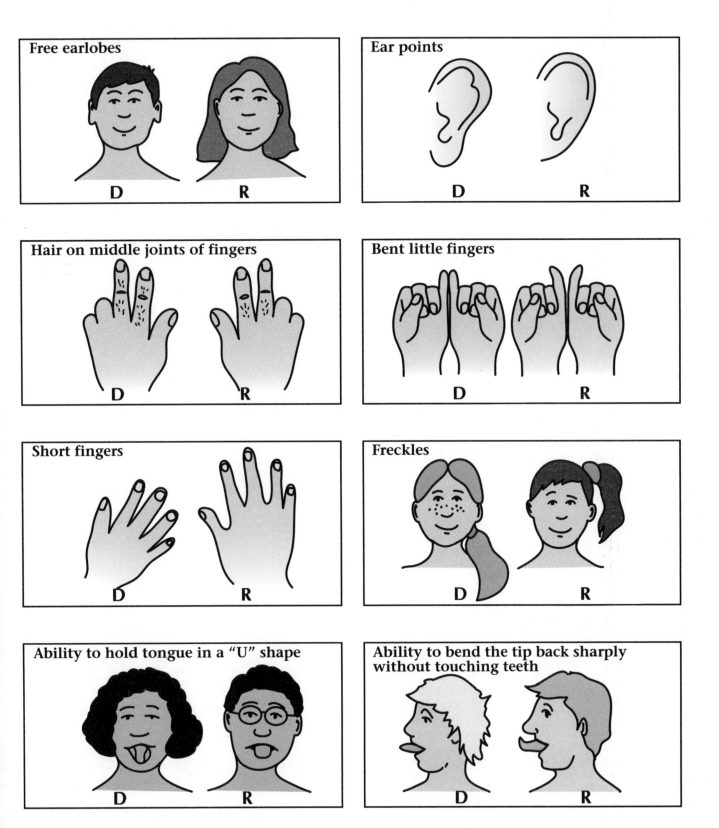

Free earlobes

D   R

Ear points

D   R

Hair on middle joints of fingers

D   R

Bent little fingers

D   R

Short fingers

D   R

Freckles

D   R

Ability to hold tongue in a "U" shape

D   R

Ability to bend the tip back sharply without touching teeth

D   R

Instruction Cards for Group Activity

Cut out the cards to use for role playing and review the different roles.

Pressure Person

You must try to get your friend to do one of the following: smoke, cheat, or go somewhere he or she doesn't want to go. Try to change your friend's mind by saying things like these:

"Please, please, please!"
"C'mon. It's easy (or fun)."
"C'mon. You'll be sorry."
"I'll be really mad if you don't."
"I won't be your friend if you don't."

The Resister

Your job is to say no to whatever the pressure person is trying to get you to do. You may need to say no more than once and in different ways.

The Coach

Your job is to watch what happens between the pressure person and the resister. If the resister seems to be having a hard time sticking with his or her decision, you can help think of ways to say no.

Try These Tongue Twisters

1. Big brown bumblebees were buried beside the bulbs on
   Bobby Brook's bulb bowls, baskets, and boxes.

2. Mr. Knox keeps his socks in a pale pink chocolate box.
   They're orange socks with spots and clocks.

3. I thought a thought.
   But the thought I thought wasn't the thought I thought I thought.
   If the thought I thought I thought had been the thought I thought, I wouldn't have
   thought so much.

4. Sheep shouldn't sleep in a shack. Sheep should sleep in a shed.

5. The beet that beat the beet that beat the other beet is now beaten by a beet that beats
   all the beets, whether the original beet that beat or the beet that beat the other beet!

6. George Gabs grabs crabs,
   Crabs George Gabs grabs.
   If George Gabs grabs crabs,
   Where are the crabs George Gabs grabs?

7. She saw the shiny soapsuds sailing down the shallow sink.

8. A fly flew past Flo's flat
   And a fly flew past flighty Flo.
   Is the fly that flew past Flo
   The same fly that flew past flighty Flo's flat?

How Am I Doing?

Every conversation can be a good experience for both the listener and the speaker. Rank how well you do in each role. During the coming week, make an effort to practice those areas that you feel are your weakest. Congratulate yourself on the areas in which you have success.

	Always	Often	Sometimes	Never
As a listener...				
1. I have good eye contact.	_____	_____	_____	_____
2. I keep an open mind about what I am being told.	_____	_____	_____	_____
3. I do not interrupt.	_____	_____	_____	_____
4. I keep to the subject.	_____	_____	_____	_____
5. I ask the speaker to explain anything I do not understand.	_____	_____	_____	_____
6. I respond with appropriate facial and body gestures.	_____	_____	_____	_____
7. I end the conversation with a warm goodbye.	_____	_____	_____	_____

	Always	Often	Sometimes	Never
As a speaker...				
1. I have a warm smile.	_____	_____	_____	_____
2. I have good eye contact.	_____	_____	_____	_____
3. I make encouraging comments.	_____	_____	_____	_____
4. I also take time to listen.	_____	_____	_____	_____
5. I make honest statements.	_____	_____	_____	_____
6. I respond cheerfully to others' comments.	_____	_____	_____	_____
7. I offer a sincere goodbye.	_____	_____	_____	_____

A Fight

Student 1:   I was just walking along minding my own business. All of a sudden you just pushed me down!

Student 2:   I didn't see you. It was an accident!

Student 1:   Well, my homework fell in a puddle, and now it's ruined! I'm going to have to do it all over again!

Student 2:   Oh sure, but you yelled at me and called me names!

Student 1:   Then you pushed me down again! On purpose!

Student 2:   This isn't the first time you've called me names! I'm tired of it!

Working It Out

What do you do when you have a problem with another person and the situation is just getting worse and worse? You can ask an adult to tell you how to make things better. Then you will have to do whatever he or she says. Or you can ask the person you are having trouble with to agree to work out a solution using the suggestions below.

You might have to go through steps 1–4 more than once. Sometimes it helps to write down what you think the problem is and share what you have written with the other person.

These are the steps for working out a problem:

1. Take turns talking about what has happened.

2. Remember to listen without interrupting.

3. Use "I" messages to express your feelings.

4. Suggest possible solutions.

5. Together agree on one solution.

If you can agree on a way to work things out, write it down, sign your name, and stick to it in the future. If the two of you can't agree on what to do, you can at least agree to try whatever an adult or another student suggests.

Living in Community

Circle the best answer.

1. A community is a group of people who

    a. have the same ideas.
    b. always treat each other well.
    c. are the same age.
    d. have something in common.

2. The traits you inherit from your parents depend on

    a. where you were born.
    b. mother's egg cell.
    c. your genes.
    d. father's sperm cell.

3. A baby begins when

    a. the mother's body makes an egg cell.
    b. the father's sperm cell joins the mother's egg cell.
    c. a mother's egg cell divides in half.
    d. the father's sperm cell enters the mother's body.

4. One healthy way to deal with differences is to

    a. pretend nothing is the matter.
    b. keep arguing about them.
    c. talk about the differences.
    d. watch TV.

5. One way you can show respect for other people is to

    a. never disagree with them.
    b. stay away from people who are different.
    c. freely use others' belongings.
    d. accept and appreciate differences among people.

6. A person with good listening skills

    a. speaks clearly.
    b. looks at the speaker and pays attention to what he or she is saying.
    c. knows a lot about many topics and tells you what you want to know.
    d. has inherited a special gene for listening.

Write your answers in complete sentences.

1. What is a Christian home?

   _____

   _____

   _____

   _____

2. Besides your family, what communities are you a part of? Name three communities. Give at least two reasons why you are a part of each of these communities.

   _____

   _____

   _____

   _____

   _____

   _____

   _____

3. What is peer pressure? Do you think peer pressure is bad or good?

   _____

   _____

   _____

4. Why do you think it is important to show respect to others?

   _____

   _____

   _____

5. What are the things you look for in a friend? Explain why each item is important.

   _____

   _____

   _____

   _____

Cell Block Pattern

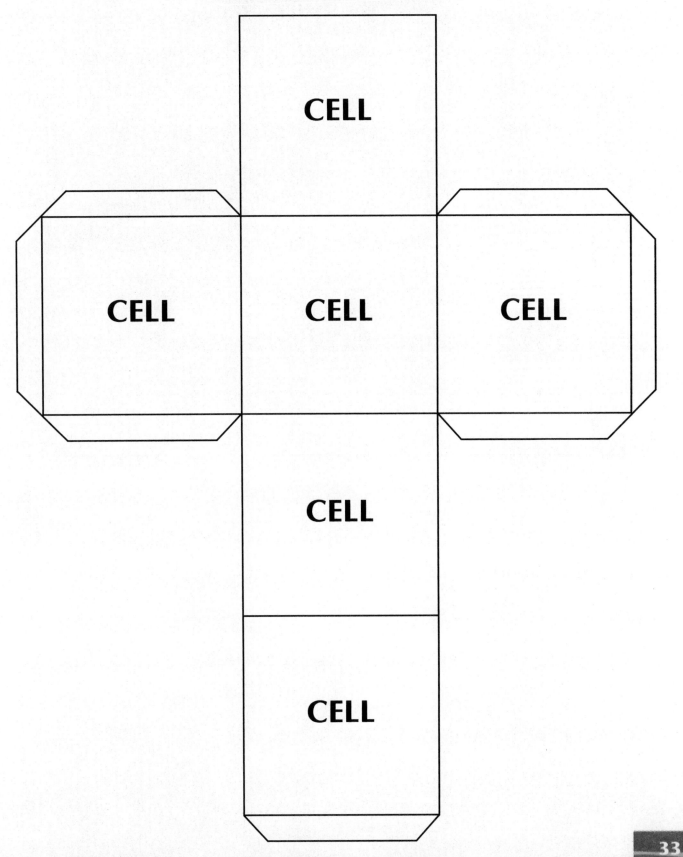

Skin Test Recording Sheet

Body Part	Distance
Finger tip	
Elbow	
Knee	
Arm	
Palm	
Lips	
Back of neck	

Where would you say was the most sensitive part of your body?

_____

What would happen if the most sensitive part was on the bottom of your feet?

_____

_____

_____

Four Kinds of Teeth

You have four kinds of teeth in your mouth. Label the types of teeth shown below.

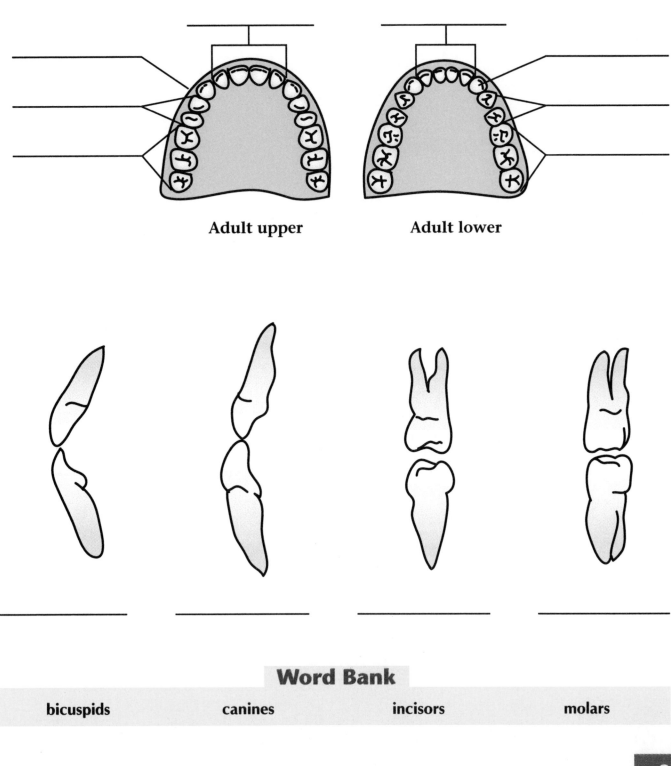

Adult upper   Adult lower

_____   _____   _____   _____

Word Bank

| bicuspids | canines | incisors | molars |

Inside Your Teeth

Your teeth are made up of layers. Label the layers and outside parts of the tooth.

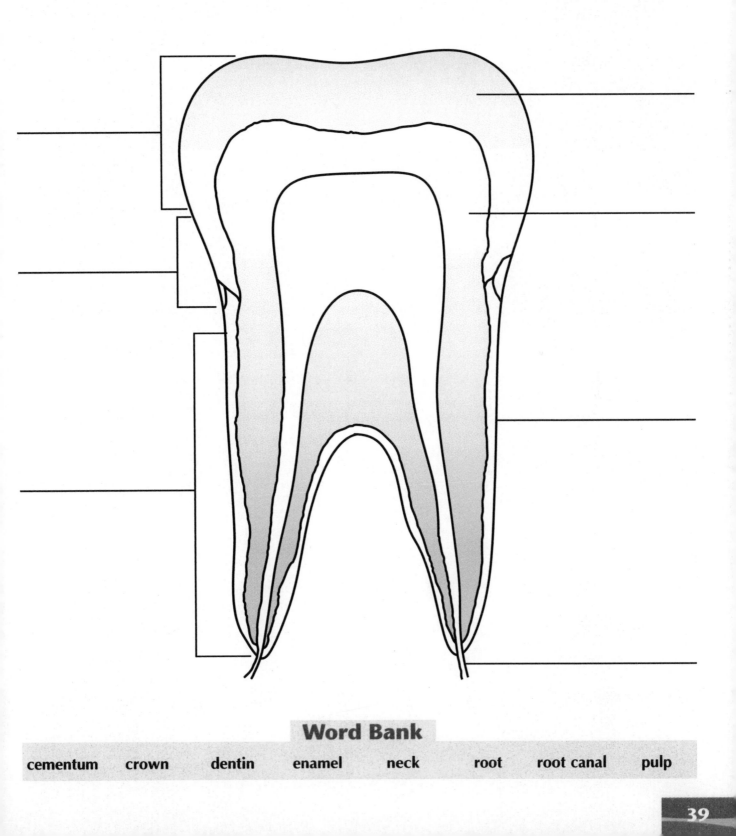

Word Bank

cementum   crown   dentin   enamel   neck   root   root canal   pulp

Looking at My Teeth

Look at your teeth. In the center of each tooth on the drawing below, write the letter that describes your tooth.

P = perfect
F = has a filling
C = has a cavity that is not filled
N = is not out yet

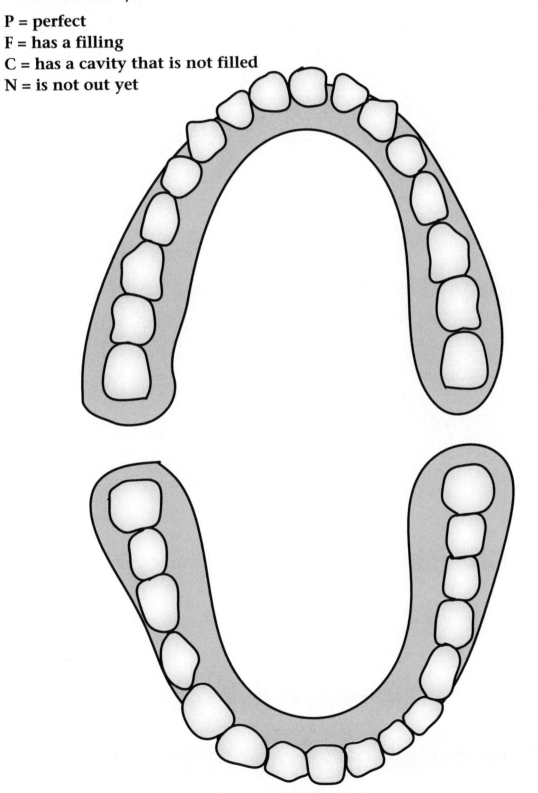

Healthy Blood Game

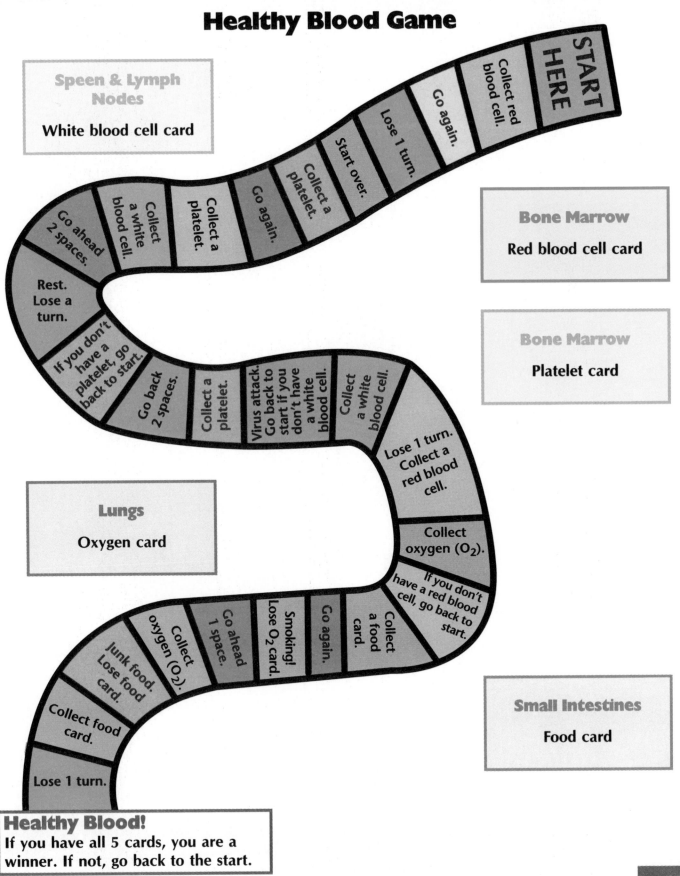

START HERE

Collect red blood cell.

Go again.

Lose 1 turn.

Start over.

Collect a platelet.

Go again.

Collect a platelet.

Collect a white blood cell.

Go ahead 2 spaces.

Rest. Lose a turn.

If you don't have a platelet, go back to start.

Go back 2 spaces.

Collect a platelet.

Virus attack. Go back to start if you don't have a white blood cell.

Collect a white blood cell.

Lose 1 turn. Collect a red blood cell.

Collect oxygen (O_2).

If you don't have a red blood cell, go back to start.

Collect a food card.

Go again.

Smoking! Lose O_2 card.

Go ahead 1 space.

Collect oxygen (O_2).

Junk food. Lose food card.

Collect food card.

Lose 1 turn.

Speen & Lymph Nodes
White blood cell card

Bone Marrow
Red blood cell card

Bone Marrow
Platelet card

Lungs
Oxygen card

Small Intestines
Food card

Healthy Blood!
If you have all 5 cards, you are a winner. If not, go back to the start.

Healthy Blood Game Cards

Cut out these game cards to use in playing the Healthy Blood game.

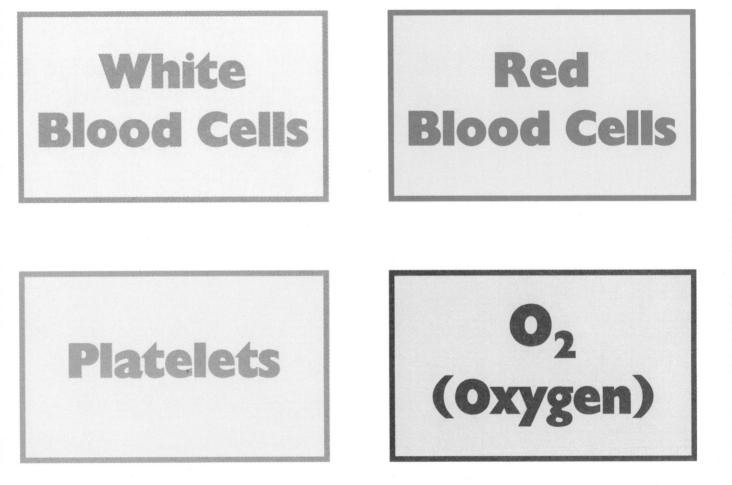

White Blood Cells

Red Blood Cells

Platelets

O_2 (Oxygen)

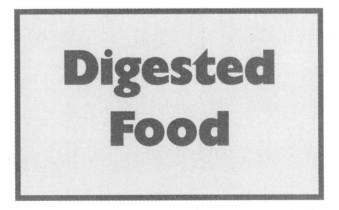

Digested Food

NAME:

The Skeletal System

Label the parts of the skeleton using words from the word bank.

Word Bank

rib	shinbone (tibia)	kneecap (patella)
skull (cranium)	tailbone (coccyx)	collarbone (clavicle
hipbone (pelvis)	jawbone (mandible)	backbone (vertebra)
thighbone (femur)	lower arm bone (radius)	shoulder blade (scapula)

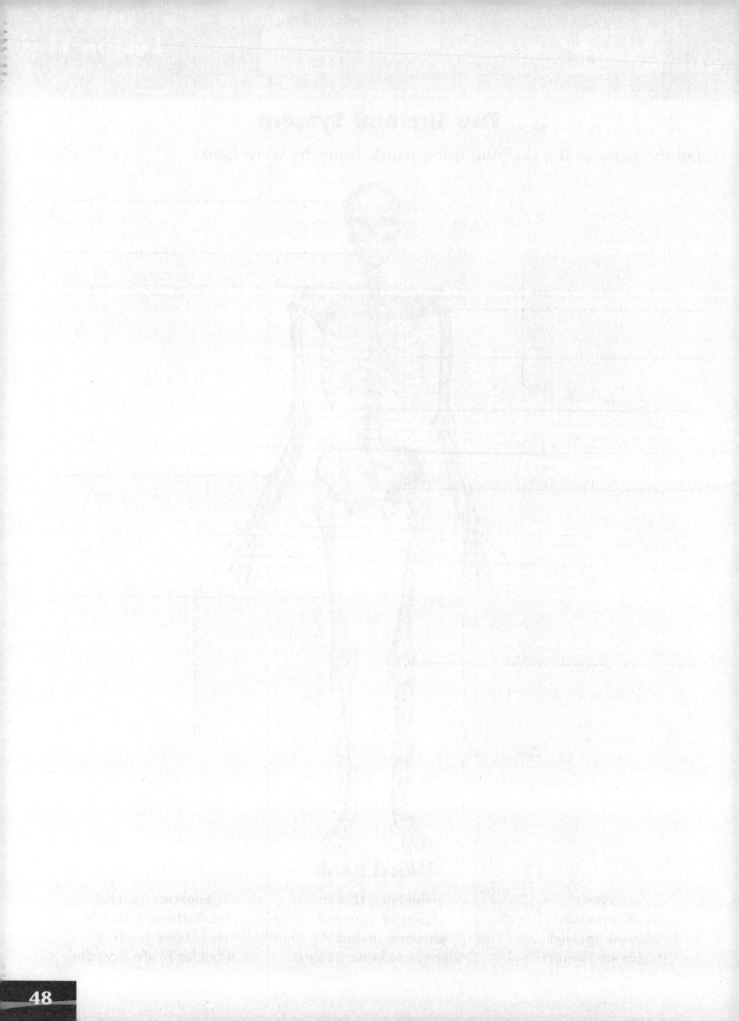

The Muscular System

Label the muscles using the words from the word bank.

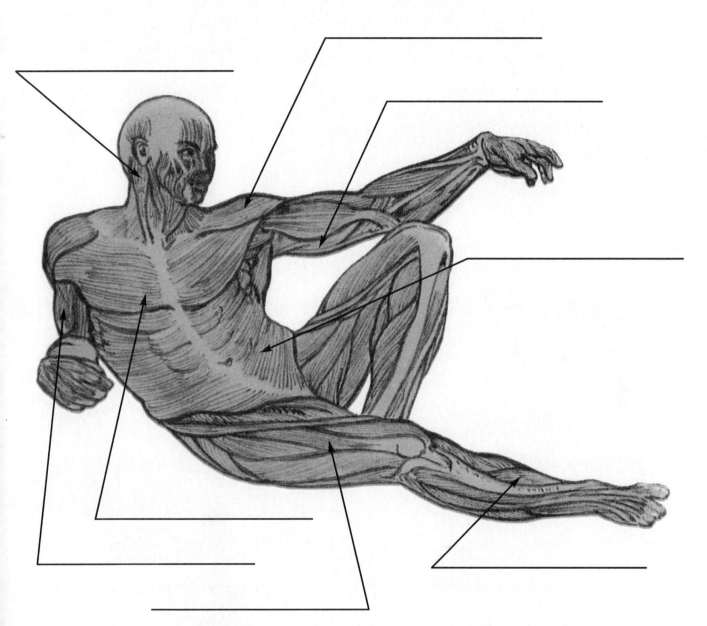

Word Bank

biceps
chest muscles (pectorals)
calf muscles (gastrocnemius)
head muscles (sternocleidomastoids)

triceps
stomach muscles
thigh muscles (quadriceps)
shoulder muscles (deltoids)

Food Testing

Record your observations on the recording sheet below.

Name of Food	Iodine Test	Paper Bag	Candle Test or Lime/Copper

The Digestive System

Label the parts of the digestive system using the words from the word bank.

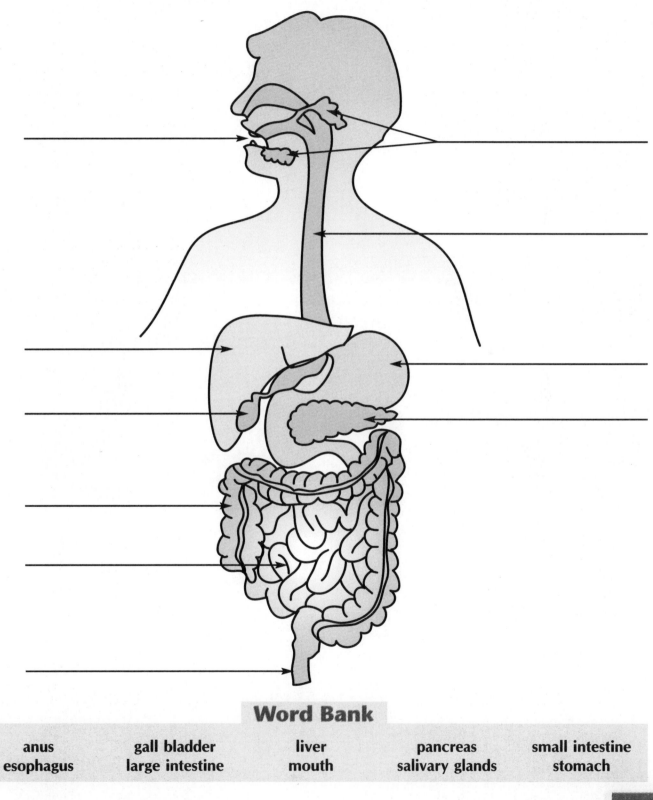

Word Bank

anus	gall bladder	liver	pancreas	small intestine
esophagus	large intestine	mouth	salivary glands	stomach

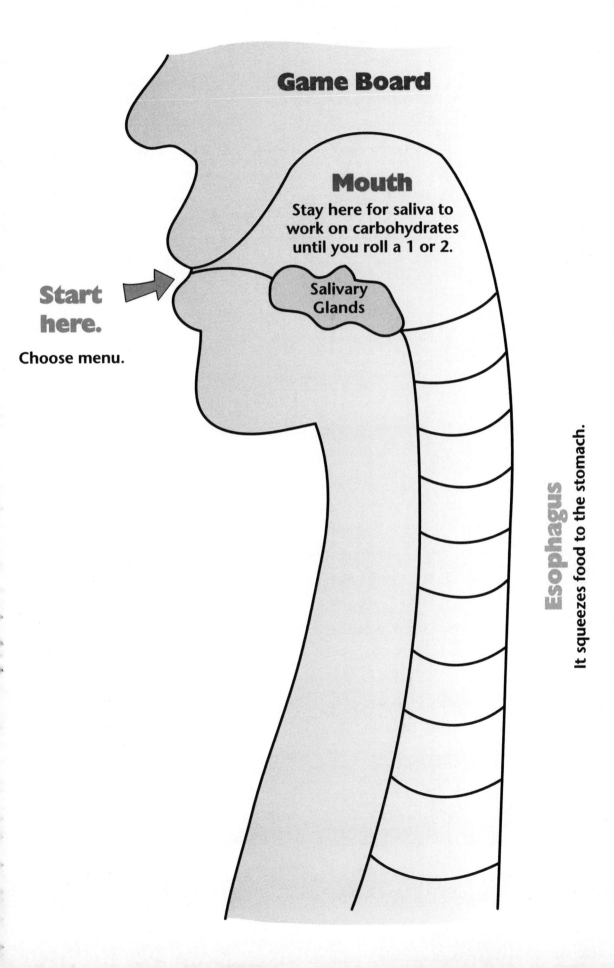

Game Board

Mouth
Stay here for saliva to work on carbohydrates until you roll a 1 or 2.

Salivary Glands

Start here.

Choose menu.

Esophagus
It squeezes food to the stomach.

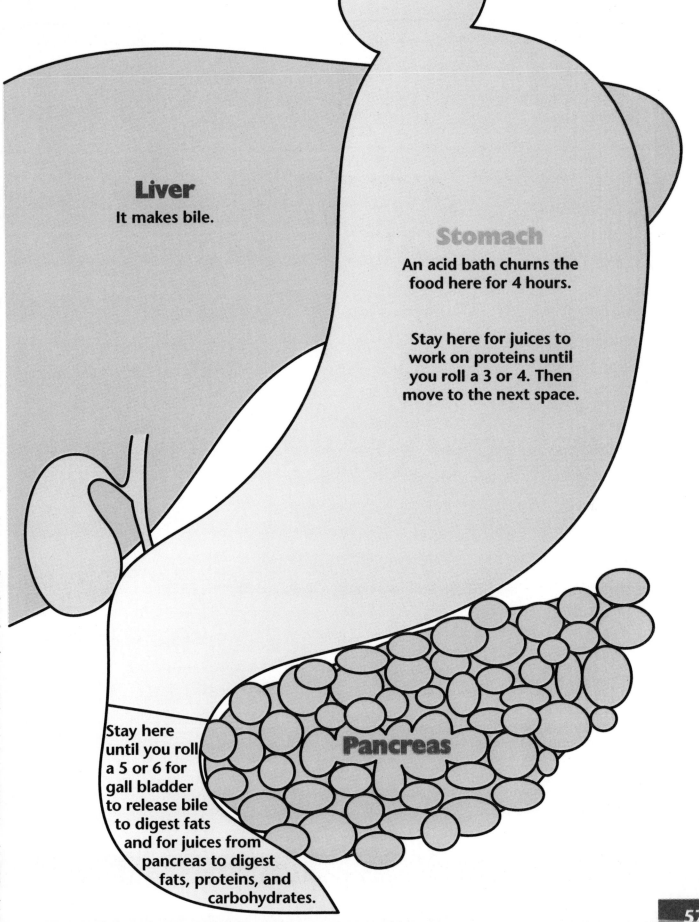

Liver
It makes bile.

Stomach

An acid bath churns the food here for 4 hours.

Stay here for juices to work on proteins until you roll a 3 or 4. Then move to the next space.

Stay here until you roll a 5 or 6 for gall bladder to release bile to digest fats and for juices from pancreas to digest fats, proteins, and carbohydrates.

Pancreas

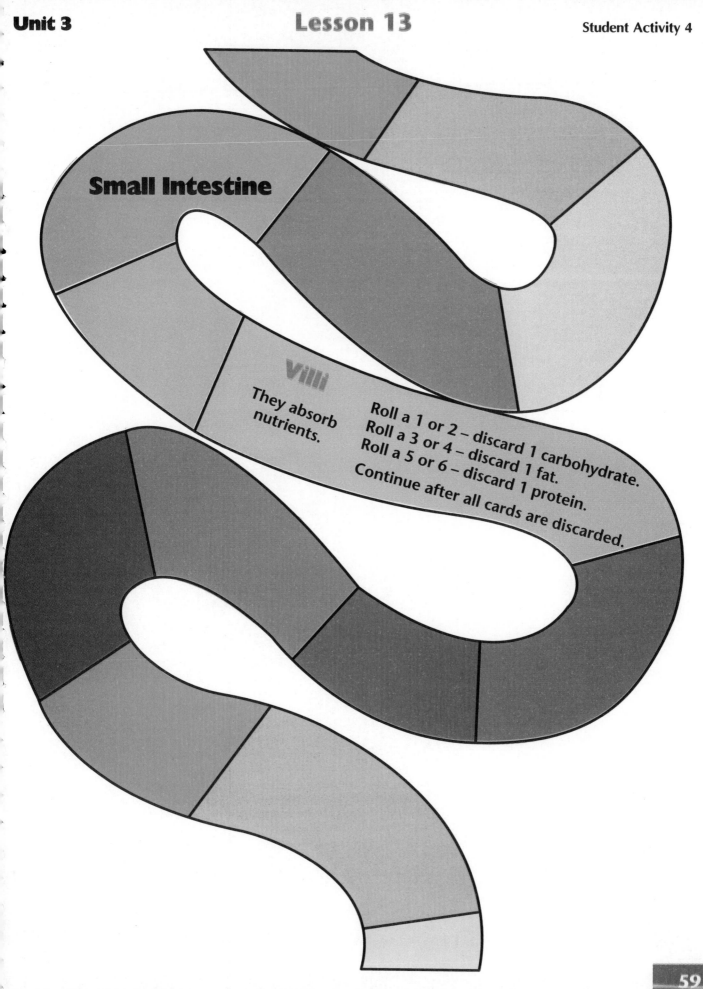

Small Intestine

Villi

They absorb nutrients.

Roll a 1 or 2 – discard 1 carbohydrate.
Roll a 3 or 4 – discard 1 fat.
Roll a 5 or 6 – discard 1 protein.
Continue after all cards are discarded.

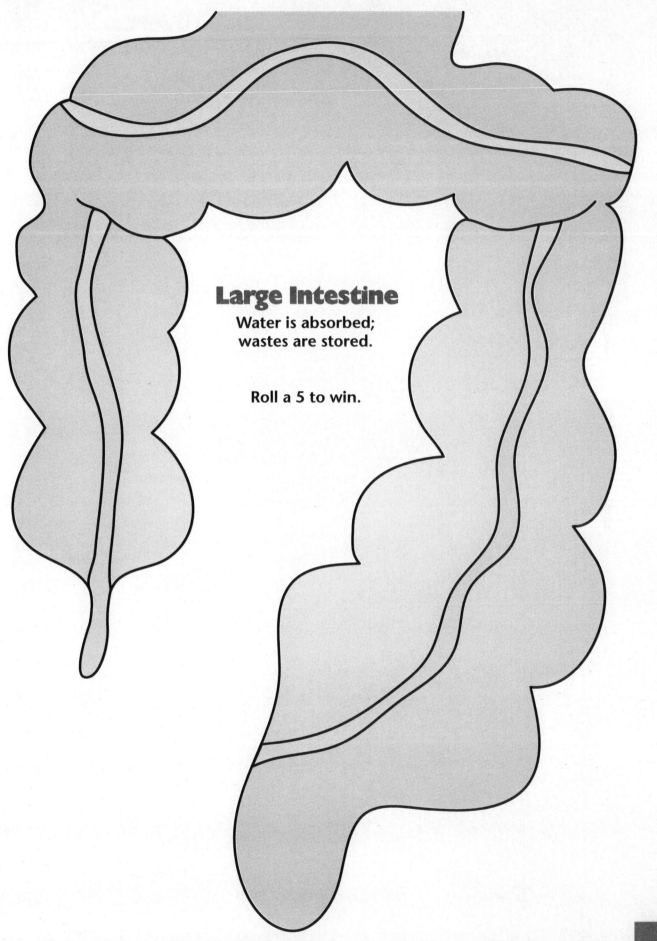

Large Intestine
Water is absorbed;
wastes are stored.

Roll a 5 to win.

Digestion Game Cards

Cut out these game cards to use in playing the Digestion game.

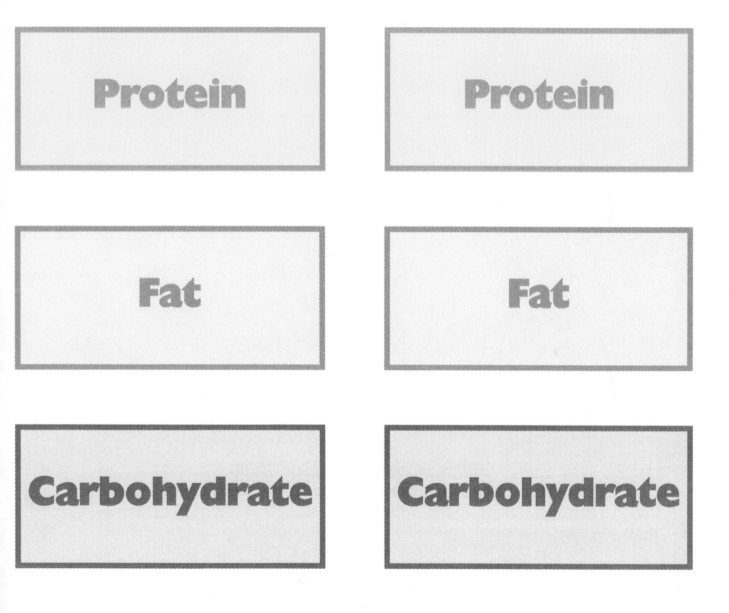

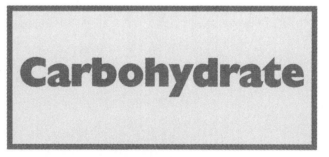

My Picnic Lunch–Playing Rules

Have fun playing this game and learning about the digestive system. Here are the game rules.

1. Decide what you want for your picnic lunch.

2. Take the right card for your lunch. Be sure to take the right number of protein, fat, and carbohydrate cards. You will keep these cards until these nutrients can be absorbed in the villi of the small intestine. The person who is able to discard all of his or her cards first, and leave the large intestine, is the winner.

3. Put your playing piece in the mouth on the same board. It must stay there for your lunch's carbohydrates to be digested. They'll be digested when you roll or a 1 or 2 on the die.

4. Move the appropriate number of spaces down the esophagus for each roll of the die until you reach the stomach.

5. Stay in the stomach for an acid bath. The stomach juices begin to work on proteins, so stay until you roll a 3 or 4 on the die.

6. When you roll a 3 or 4, move one space to the beginning of the small intestine. Here the gall bladder sends in bile made in the liver. This aids in digesting fat. And the pancreas makes several juices that digest proteins, fats, and carbohydrates. Stay here until you roll a 5 or 6.

7. Move the right number of spaces down the small intestine until you get to the villi. Stay there until you can discard all the cards you had at the beginning. The card that you discard is determined by the number you roll on the die.

1 or 2 – discard	3 or 4 – discard	5 or 6 – discard
1 carbohydrate card	1 fat card	1 protein card

After discarding all nutrient cards, move on to the large intestine. Stay there for water to be reabsorbed and for waste storage until you roll a 5. Then you can leave the body and you are a winner!

"Picnic lunch" menu:	Nutrient cards needed:
Choice #1	(6)
Tuna with mayonnaise on wheat bread	Protein/carbohydrate/fat
Potato chips	Carbohydrate/fat
Skimmed milk	Protein
Choice #2	(6)
Peanut butter and jelly on wheat bread	Protein/carbohydrate/fat
Brownie	Carbohydrate/fat
Orange juice	Carbohydrate
Choice #3	(6)
Submarine sandwich with mustard	Protein/carbohydrate/fat
Chocolate chip cookie	Carbohydrate/fat
Pop (Coke® or Sprite®, etc.)	Carbohydrate

How My Body Works

Write short answers to these questions.

1. What are the three main parts of the cell? _____

    _____

2. What is the job of the nucleus? _____

    _____

3. List at least three ways your skin helps you.

    _____

    _____

    _____

4. What are two important jobs of your hair? _____

    _____

5. List at least four things you can do to prevent tooth decay.

    _____

    _____

    _____

    _____

Fill in the word from the word bank that best completes each sentence. The word bank has more words than you need.

Word Bank

bicuspid	cell	epiglottis	molars	tendons
canine	dentin	joint	plaque	tissue
capillaries	enamel	pulp	scapula	trachea

1. Each person starts as one _____ .

2. Cells with the same job group together to make body _____ .

3. The soft core of the tooth is the _____ .

4. _____ is the hard outside layer of a tooth.

5. Bacteria on your teeth form a soft, sticky layer called _____ .

6. A _____ tooth has a sharp point for tearing food.

7. _____ are wide, bumpy teeth, perfect for grinding.

8. A _____ has two sharp points for crushing.

9. _____ attach muscles to bones.

10. A _____ is the name of the place where two bones meet.

11. The tiniest blood vessels are called _____ .

12. The _____ covers the windpipe to keep out food.

Use complete sentences to write your answer to each of the following questions.

1. Tell how the virus called HIV causes AIDS.

_____

_____

_____

2. Describe the word of the body's circulatory system.

_____

_____

_____

3. Tell about the job of bones in the body.

_____

_____

_____

4. Explain how muscles move the body.

_____

_____

_____

5. Explain what the digestive system does.

_____

_____

_____

_____

Shaina's Nutrients Shelves

Shaina has just finished her grocery shopping. Help her place the foods below on the "nutrient shelves" where they belong by writing the name of each food in the right place.

Baked beans
Blueberries
Bagels
Broccoli
Cantaloupe
Carrots

Cheddar cheese
Chicken
Cornflakes
Eggs
Green beans

Hamburger
Ice cream
Milk
Muffins
Orange juice
Peanuts

Tomatoes
Tuna fish
Waffles
Wheat bread
Yogurt

FOODS HAVING PROTEIN

FOODS HAVING VITAMINS A AND C

FOODS HAVING CALCIUM

FOODS HAVING CARBOHYDRATES

How Did Leo Do Today?

Here is a list of what Leo ate in one day. Read over the list and then answer the questions below.

| Grains | Vegetables | Fruits | Milk | Meat & Beans |

Breakfast	**Lunch**	**Dinner**	**Snacks**
slice of toast	donut	meatballs	potato chips
milk	orange juice	rice	milk
	candy bar	green beans	

1. How much did Leo have of each of the five food groups?

   _____ grain group

   _____ fruit group

   _____ vegetable group

   _____ milk/yogurt/cheese group

   _____ meat & beans group

2. How many foods did Leo eat that are considered fats or sweets? List them below.

   _____

3. Which groups does Leo need more of? How much more?

   _____

   _____

4. Suggest foods that could make Leo's list provide a balanced daily diet.

   _____

   _____

   _____

   _____

   _____

Where's the Sugar Hiding?

Read each label carefully. Circle any sugars that are hiding in these foods.

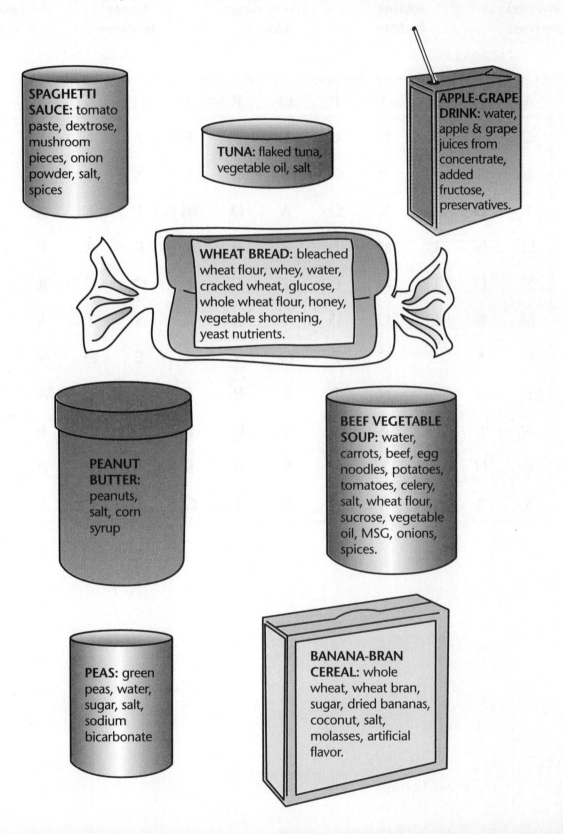

SPAGHETTI SAUCE: tomato paste, dextrose, mushroom pieces, onion powder, salt, spices

TUNA: flaked tuna, vegetable oil, salt

APPLE-GRAPE DRINK: water, apple & grape juices from concentrate, added fructose, preservatives.

WHEAT BREAD: bleached wheat flour, whey, water, cracked wheat, glucose, whole wheat flour, honey, vegetable shortening, yeast nutrients.

PEANUT BUTTER: peanuts, salt, corn syrup

BEEF VEGETABLE SOUP: water, carrots, beef, egg noodles, potatoes, tomatoes, celery, salt, wheat flour, sucrose, vegetable oil, MSG, onions, spices.

PEAS: green peas, water, sugar, salt, sodium bicarbonate

BANANA-BRAN CEREAL: whole wheat, wheat bran, sugar, dried bananas, coconut, salt, molasses, artificial flavor.

The words for sugar that appear on most food labels are hidden in the word search. Use the word bank to find and circle them. Not all of the words will be used.

Word Bank

molasses dextrose	sucrose lactose	corn syrup glucose	honey fructose	maltose sugar

```
A  R  S  T  P  O  P  I  D  A  R  E
G  J  X  U  C  O  S  E  E  L  E  O
L  I  G  P  G  S  C  S  X  O  O  R
T  D  L  K  O  A  O  M  T  L  N  S
O  N  U  M  E  R  R  O  R  A  P  A
S  D  C  N  C  T  N  L  O  C  R  L
N  B  O  U  D  Y  S  A  S  T  A  V
C  I  S  R  E  O  Y  S  E  O  N  Y
E  R  E  N  L  E  R  S  H  S  W  S
A  L  O  A  N  S  U  E  G  E  E  P
R  H  T  Y  V  R  P  S  A  M  P  O
S  J  F  R  U  C  T  O  S  E  S  N
```

Mold! Ugh, Ugh, and Yuck!

Write the name of your food.	Describe what the fresh food looks like.	Describe what the spoiled food looks like.	Where do you think this food should be stored?

Menu Sheet

Food	Food Group	Amount	Nutrients

Food for a Healthy Me

Matching. Match the words with the correct meaning. Write the letter in the blank.

1. _____ proteins

2. _____ minerals

3. _____ carbohydrates

4. _____ vitamins

5. _____ water

6. _____ fats

a. necessary for each body process and to digest food

b. help the body fight disease and use proteins, fats, and carbohydrates

c. build and repair body tissue and fight infection

d. main source of energy

e. help other nutrients do their work and control many body activities

f. energy reserve and store vitamins

Short Answer.

1. Write the name of the food group in the correct space.

1.	2.	3.	4.	5.

2. Name three diseases that are caused by a lack of nutrients.

_____

_____

_____

True or False.

_____ 1. Foods will spoil if they are not preserved.

_____ 2. Some foods can stay fresh for several months if they are carefully stored.

_____ 3. Some foods will never spoil.

_____ 4. Microorganisms such as bacteria cause food to spoil.

_____ 5. Pasteurized milk doesn't need to be kept cold.

_____ 6. Food poisoning never happens in North America.

_____ 7. Drying, smoking, pickling, and canning are some ways to preserve foods.

Short Essay.

What do you think is the purpose of food? _____

_____

_____

_____

_____

_____

_____

_____

_____

_____

_____

An Accident Waiting to Happen

Clap once for each X. Emphasize the words with the accent marks over them.

Introduction

Do you wánt to bléed? Do you wánt to díe?
Do you líke to húrt? Do you líke to crý?
Better stráighten out your thínking,
Or you míght be blínking,
ítty-bitty téar drops óut of your éyes!

1. If you dón't know the fácts,
   And you dón't know the rúles,
   Better wáit! Hésitate! *(Pause.)*
   Chéck the láke befóre you díve; *X*
   Tést the íce before you skáte, *X*
   Or it júst might bé too láte! *XX*
   Withóut the proper clúes, you'll be ín for bad néws. *XX*

Chorus

Tooooooo bád! Soooooo sád!
'Cause I'm bád, *X* I'm bád, bád néws! *XX*
I'm an áccident wáiting to háppen, *X*
And you bétter bewáre, *(Pause.)* 'cause if you don't take cáre,
I júst might háppen to yóu! *XX*

2. If you cán't stay awáke,
   Or you're ín a mad rúsh,
   Better wáit! Hésitate! *(Pause.)*
   Pay clóse attention to the thíngs you dó! *X*
   Wátch the róad when ón your bíke! *X*
   Sígnal every túrn you máke; *XX*
   Or whát might be a-cóming, might be cómin', cómin' at yóu!

Bridge

And whén you're in the cár do you thínk to buckle úp?
Do you thínk to see that othérs do, tóo? *X*
And whén you're in the stréet are you súre of where you áre
Or áre you in the páthway of a trúck or twó?

(Back to the chorus.)

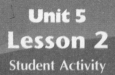

Safety Inspection

Playground hazards to look for:

1. Bent, warped, or rusted parts
2. Open hooks, links, or rings
3. Worn swing chains or hangers
4. Loose or heavy swing seats
5. Swing seats with sharp edges or corners
6. Broken supports or anchors
7. Any sharp edge or point
8. Exposed ends that should be covered by plugs or caps
9. Bolt ends that should be covered by plugs or caps
10. Loose bolts or nuts
11. Nails sticking out
12. Splintered wood
13. Rotted wood
14. Worn parts
15. Broken or missing rails, steps, rungs, or seats
16. Ground cover worn or scattered
17. Chipped or peeling paint
18. Trash or broken glass on ground
19. Tripping hazards (roots, rocks, boards)
20. Wet areas

Other hazards you noticed:

_____

_____

_____

_____

_____

_____

What Do You Know About Fire Safety?

Read the statements and decide whether they are true or false. If a statement is false, rewrite it to make it true.

T   F   Smoke stays near the floor, so in a fire stand as tall as you can.

_____

_____

T   F   Because you don't know where a fire will start, it doesn't help to plan how to escape from a house.

_____

_____

T   F   If your clothes catch on fire, running makes the fire burn faster.

_____

_____

T   F   If there's a fire in your house, quickly get the telephone book, find the right number, and call the fire department.

_____

_____

T   F   Because one smoke detector makes so much noise, each house only needs one smoke detector.

_____

_____

What's Your Story?

Write about a fire that you know about. Tell what happened. What caused the fire? How do you think the fire could have been prevented?

Home Alone Safety

Fill in the blanks. Then find the same words hidden in the word search.

1. On the way home from school, walk with one or two _____ .

2. Don't let a _____ know you are home _____ .

3. If someone calls and asks to talk with your _____ , say that your parents can't come to the phone now. Ofter to take a _____ .

4. _____ all telephone calls.

5. Follow _____ rules for having friends over.

6. Keep a _____ of helpful _____ _____ near the phone.

7. When you're home alone, don't _____ the door to strangers.

L	P	N	A	S	O	N	E	P	B	S	A
M	O	A	R	H	T	R	L	A	E	N	S
O	N	S	N	E	D	R	S	N	A	L	E
N	E	C	U	B	P	P	A	R	E	N	T
S	F	E	M	N	I	S	R	N	J	I	M
R	A	E	B	M	L	O	U	R	G	M	S
O	M	T	E	L	E	P	H	O	N	E	R
A	I	M	R	W	A	E	K	E	L	S	R
R	L	I	S	T	R	N	S	N	I	S	E
U	Y	O	N	V	E	D	S	T	R	A	M
B	A	Y	N	I	N	R	D	W	V	G	W
P	O	N	R	E	K	I	A	S	E	E	Y
N	E	A	I	D	M	F	R	U	B	R	O
W	C	R	F	A	N	D	C	E	R	S	T
A	F	R	U	Y	O	T	P	N	O	D	P

Family Home-Alone Rules

Fill this out with your family. What does your family expect of you when you are home alone? Talk about the following areas.

1. Using the stove and/or microwave

   _____

   _____

2. Doing homework

   _____

   _____

3. Asking friends over

   _____

   _____

4. Using the telephone

   _____

   _____

5. Taking medicine

   _____

   _____

6. Other family rules:

   _____

   _____

   Important telephone numbers:

   Relatives: _____

   Emergency:_____

   Other: _____

Better Safe Than Sorry

Matching. Match the words with the correct meaning. Write the letter in the blank.

1. _____ ride out
2. _____ hazard
3. _____ PFD
4. _____ stop, drop, and roll
5. _____ smoke detector

a. something that sets off an alarm if smoke is present
b. a danger or risk
c. personal flotation device
d. the best way to put out fire on clothing
e. to ride a bike onto a road without stopping and looking for cars

Short Answer. Answer the following questions.

1. What do the letters SIPDA stand for?

   S _____

   I _____

   P _____

   D _____

   A _____

2. What can you do to help drivers of cars and trucks see you during the day? How about at night? _____

   _____

3. When does a person need to wear a PFD? Why does a person need to wear one?

   _____

   _____

4. What is the meaning of this water safety rule: "Reach or throw, don't go"?

   _____

   _____

Short Essay. Answer these questions using complete sentences.

1. Is there a place on your school playground or neighborhood park that is unsafe? If the answer is "yes," explain what it is and what you think should be done about it. If the answer is "no," explain what your school or neighborhood has done to keep the environment safe for kids.

_____

_____

_____

_____

_____

2. Write at least three rules that you should follow if your are home alone.

_____

_____

_____

_____

_____

3. Explain the difference between a "good touch" and a "bad touch."

_____

_____

_____

_____

_____

4. Tell two good ways that people can prevent accidents.

_____

_____

_____

_____

_____

Over-the-Counter Medicines

Find three OTCs your family uses. Read the label of each OTC and fill in the blanks.

OTC name _____

   What it does _____

   Directions for using: adult _____

                               child _____

                               infant _____

   Side effects _____

   Warnings or cautions _____

   Have you used this OTC? _____

   Does it do what it claims? Explain. _____

_____

OTC name _____

   What it does _____

   Directions for using: adult _____

                                 child _____

                               infant _____

   Side effects _____

   Warnings or cautions _____

   Have you used this OTC? _____

   Does it do what it claims? Explain. _____

_____

OTC name _____

   What it does _____

   Directions for using: adult _____

                               child _____

                               infant _____

   Side effects _____

   Warnings or cautions _____

   Have you used this OTC? _____

   Does it do what it claims? Explain. _____

_____

Cigarettes: Behind the Smoke Screen

Read what some people have to say about smoking. Decide if you agree or disagree with them. Put a check in the right box.

	Agree	Disagree	Don't Know
1. Smoking relaxes people.	☐	☐	☐
2. Most people smoke, so it can't be that bad.	☐	☐	☐
3. People who don't smoke usually live longer than people who do.	☐	☐	☐
4. Other people's smoking won't hurt me.	☐	☐	☐
5. Nicotine in cigarette smoke makes the heart beat too fast.	☐	☐	☐
6. Smoking aggravates emphysema and bronchitis.	☐	☐	☐
7. Cigarettes are not as harmful as pipes and cigars.	☐	☐	☐
8. Smoking helps you lose weight.	☐	☐	☐
9. Many long-term smokers have a cough.	☐	☐	☐
10. More people than ever are kicking the smoking habit.	☐	☐	☐

"Cigarettes: Behind the Smoke Screen" from Lungs Are for Life. Copyright © 1988 by the American Lung Association. Reprinted with permission.

Cigarettes: Behind the Smoke Screen

1. **Smoking relaxes people.**

   Disagree. Nicotine contained in tobacco smoke is a stimulant, not a sedative. After even a few drags, the nicotine in smoke stimulates the heart to pump harder. When people say they are relaxed by smoking, they mean one of two things: 1) taking the time to smoke relaxes them; 2) it is relaxing to satisfy the craving for nicotine.

2. **Most people smoke, so it can't be that bad.**

   Disagree. Less than one in three adults smoke. If you take the whole population, smokers are probably one in five.

3. **People who don't smoke usually live longer than people who do.**

   Agree. The average male non-smoker stands to gain about eight years of life.

4. **Other people's smoking won't hurt me.**

   Disagree. It's not likely that a person who just breathes in other people's smoke will get diseases like cancer or emphysema. But asthma and other respiratory sufferers find their conditions worsened by smoke in a room. Also children of heavy smokers suffer from more frequent and severe colds and respiratory infections.

5. **Nicotine in cigarette smoke makes the heart beat too fast.**

   Agree. Nicotine stimulates the heart to beat fast. At the same time, nicotine makes blood vessels narrow, thus reducing circulation. The combination of these effects puts a great deal of pressure on the heart and blood vessels. This is a key reason why smokers suffer more heart trouble.

6. **Smoking aggravates emphysema and bronchitis.**

   Agree. Smoke from cigarettes aggravates the whole respiratory system. "Tar" and chemicals in smoke may hurt the delicate cilia and alveoli, cutting off oxygen. These parts can even be destroyed. These are among the causes of bronchitis and emphysema.

7. **Cigarettes are not as harmful as pipes and cigars.**

   Disagree. Direct inhalation of the smoke is what damages lungs most. Cigarette smokers who tend to inhale suffer the most. But pipe and cigar smokers who inhale also suffer. Smokers who do not directly inhale take in smoke anyway—though less. However, research points to greater incidence of oral cancers (mouth, tongue, lips) for pipe and cigar smokers.

8. **Smoking helps you lose weight.**

   Disagree. It is true that smoking reduces a person's sense of taste and smell. These senses are related to pleasure n eating. But look at the greater number of overweight smokers will dispel the myth of smoking as they key to dieting. Some people, it's true, gain weight when they give up smoking. Yet in a total program of personal health, a person learns how to moderate food intake when kicking the smoking habit.

9. **Many long-term smokers have a cough.**

   Agree. Because the cilia are harmed by tar and nicotine, they can't do a good job of keeping dirt away from the lungs. Therefore, the smoker's body naturally ties another defense—coughing.

10. **More people than ever are kicking the smoking habit.**

    Agree. Recent studies show that as people become more aware of the dangers related to smoking, more people manage to kick the habit. Last year over two million smokers stopped. However, the number of teenage girls who smoke cigarettes grew. In fact, this is the first time in history that females in any age group outnumbered male smokers.

"Cigarettes: Behind the Smoke Screen" from Lungs Are for Life. Copyright © 1988 by the American Lung Association. Reprinted with permission.

What Do You Think?

Read what some people have to say about alcohol. Decide if you agree or disagree with them. Put a check in the right box.

	Agree	Disagree	Don't Know
1. Alcohol makes you warm.	☐	☐	☐
2. Alcohol is a drug.	☐	☐	☐
3. Root beer has alcohol in it.	☐	☐	☐
4. Alcohol affects everyone the same way.	☐	☐	☐
5. People can drive well after drinking if they concentrate.	☐	☐	☐
6. Only people who live on the streets of big cities have problems with alcohol.	☐	☐	☐
7. Alcohol slows a person down.	☐	☐	☐
8. Drinking is what makes a party fun.	☐	☐	☐
9. Alcohol is especially dangerous for young people.	☐	☐	☐
10. Alcoholics can be cured if they have only one drink daily.	☐	☐	☐

What Do You Think?

1. **Alcohol makes you warm.**

   Disagree. Alcohol actually lowers body temperature. That's why drinking in very cold weather can be dangerous.

2. **Alcohol is a drug.**

   Agree. Alcohol is a substance that changes the way a person thinks, feels, and acts.

3. **Root beer has alcohol in it.**

   Disagree. Root beer is a soft drink that contains no alcohol.

4. **Alcohol affects everyone the same way.**

   Disagree. Alcohol affects everyone differently depending on how much and how quickly the person drinks, how much the person weighs, how the person feels while drinking, and if the person eats while drinking (food makes alcohol enter the bloodstream more slowly).

5. **People can drive well after drinking if they concentrate.**

   Disagree. People may think they're able to drive well, but they're wrong. Alcohol can seriously affect vision, judgment, and reaction time.

6. **Only people who live on the streets of big cities have problems with alcohol.**

   Disagree. Many problem drinkers and alcoholics have families, friends, and jobs. Anyone can have a problem with alcohol.

7. **Alcohol slows a person down.**

   Agree. Alcohol slows down the brain, which in turn slows down on how a person thinks, moves, and talks.

8. **Drinking is what makes a party fun.**

   Disagree. You don't need alcohol to have a good time. There are many ways to relax and have fun without drinking.

9. **Alcohol is especially dangerous for young people.**

   Agree. Young people become drunk more quickly from less alcohol than adults. Because young people usually weigh less than adults and have smaller livers, their blood alcohol content rises faster when they drink. Besides, young people who drink are breaking the law. Tell students what the legal drinking age is in your state. Note that research shows that when states changed the drinking age from 18 to 21, the number of accidents, injuries, and death among young people went down.

10. **Alcoholics can be cured by cutting down to one drink a day.**

   Disagree. There is no cure for alcoholism. The only treatment for alcoholism is to stop drinking and never take another drink—not even a small one.

Drug Safety Puzzle

Use the clues to complete the puzzle.

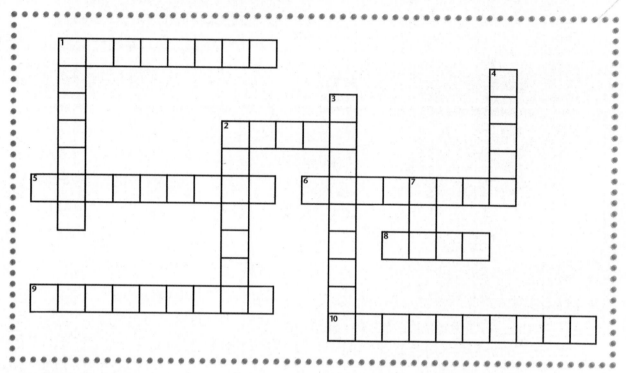

Across

1. When a person comes to depend on a drug and can't live without it, he or she is

   _____ .

2. Tiny hairs in the body that keep dust and germs out of the lungs.

5. When people take a drug for a long time, their bodies need more and more of the drug. This is called _____ .

6. Drug in tobacco that makes the heart work much faster than normal.

8. A substance other than food that changes the way the body works.

9. Drugs used to prevent or treat sickness or to stop pain.

10. A sickness in which people come to depend on alcohol.

Down

1. A drug found in beer, wine, and liquor.

2. A powerful drug made from the cocoa plant.

3. A drug that makes it hard for people to learn and remember.

4. To use a drug in ways that harm one's health.

7. A brown substance in tobacco smoke that sticks to the lungs and harms them.

Staying on the Right Track

Matching. Match the words with the correct meaning. Write the letter in the blank.

1. _____ OTC

2. _____ alcohol

3. _____ cocaine

4. _____ tar

5. _____ medicine

6. _____ prescription medicine

7. _____ marijuana

8. _____ nicotine

9. _____ side effects

a. a drug used for health reasons

b. a dangerous drug made from the cocoa plant

c. medicine ordered by a doctor for a certain person

d. unwanted changes that can be caused by a medicine

e. a substances that changes the way a person thinks, feels, and acts

f. a medicine a person can buy without a prescription

g. substance in tobacco smoke that harms the cilia in the lungs

h. a substance made from a plant and smoked; it contains a drug that changes a person's mood

i. substance in tobacco that makes the heart work faster than normal.

Short Answer.

1. What different ways can people take medicines into the body? _____

   _____

   _____

2. What are three rules to help you use medicines safely?

   _____

   _____

   _____

3. Name three harmful substances in tobacco smoke.

   _____

   _____

   _____

4. Why is it unsafe to drink alcohol and then drive a car? _____

_____

_____

Short Essay. Answer these questions using complete sentences.

1. Describe what addiction is. _____

_____

_____

_____

2. Why do you think people take drugs? _____

_____

_____

_____

The Case of the Healthyway Baby

Kids at school have been calling me Detective Newt these days. (Short for nutrition. Dumb joke, isn't it?) See, I cracked the Healthyway Case. You must have read the story in the papers. You know, the one about the missing one-year-old baby who's going to inherit the Healthyway family fortune.

Well, let me start at the beginning. I have this paper route. And sometimes I get kind of bored just walking around delivering papers. So I started thinking of each house on my route as a person. The tiny pink house is just a baby, like my sister Sue. The solid brick house with the square bushes is a serious and sober person, like my Aunt Kate. The yellow house with lots of flowers in its window boxes is cheerful and sunny, just like Mr. Gordon, my piano teacher. And so on. But one house I couldn't pin down. Something about it just didn't add up. There was something fishy about it. I started thinking of the house as a big question mark.

Then last Saturday I got a break. I was collecting for the paper. Lots of people were outside working in the yard or just enjoying the spring sun. But when I came to the question-mark house all was quiet. Nothing much was going on there. I stood for a moment at the back door, feeling a little uneasy. Finally I rang the bell.

A guy with terrible teeth opened the door. Said he was Mr. Cookie Dough. Said to come in while he got the cash. I stepped into the kitchen. Open boxes of cookies and piles of candy bars were sitting all over the counters. Mr. Dough saw my surprised look. "Have some," he said. "We never touch fruits and vegetables. We just leave boxes of stuff around, and we all help ourselves. Easier that way. Like something to drink, too?"

He opened the refrigerator, and I peeked past him. It was chock full of soda pop. No milk or orange juice in sight.

Just then a girl (I think her name was Fudge) walked into the kitchen. She whined to her father, "How about some quarters for the candy machine at the mall? C'mon."

I took the chance to slide past Mr. Dough and glance into the living room. A crabby kid of about five or six was fighting with another kid of about the same age. An older boy—with caved-in shoulders and a dull look—was just sitting there watching them.

Then I saw the rosy-cheeked baby. His hair was shining in the sunlight. He was holding onto a teddy bear and bouncing up and down, up and down. Wow! What energy! His eyes were dancing as he looked about, enjoying himself.

All of a sudden I knew. I took the money and told him I had lots more places to collect and didn't have time for the drink. I tore out there, jumped on my bike, rode home, and called the police. "I've found Bouncer Healthyway," I told them. I had just solved the case of the Healthyway baby.

How did "Detective Newt" spot the Healthyway baby? Name at least four clues.

_____

_____

_____

_____

_____

_____

_____

Choose Physical Fitness

Write on the chart the physical activities you usually do on a weekday.

What's the activity?	How many minutes?
_____	_____
_____	_____
_____	_____
_____	_____

Answer these questions using complete sentences.

1. How much time to you usually spend on a weekday doing physical activities?

    _____

2. What areas of physical fitness do each activity help to develop?

    _____

    _____

3. What areas of fitness do you think need more attention?

    _____

    _____

4. What other activities can you do each day to improve your fitness? Describe at least four.

    _____

    _____

    _____

    _____

    _____

My Plan for Personal Health Care

Personal habits are important for good health. What will you do each day in each of the areas below?

1. To take good care of my skin, I will

   _____

   _____

   _____

2. To take good care of my hair, I will

   _____

   _____

   _____

3. To take good care of my nails, I will

   _____

   _____

   _____

4. To make sure I get enough rest, I will

   _____

   _____

   _____

5. Make a plan for doing these personal care activities each day. Write your plan on the chart.

Here's My Plan	
Time	Activity

My Social Support Network

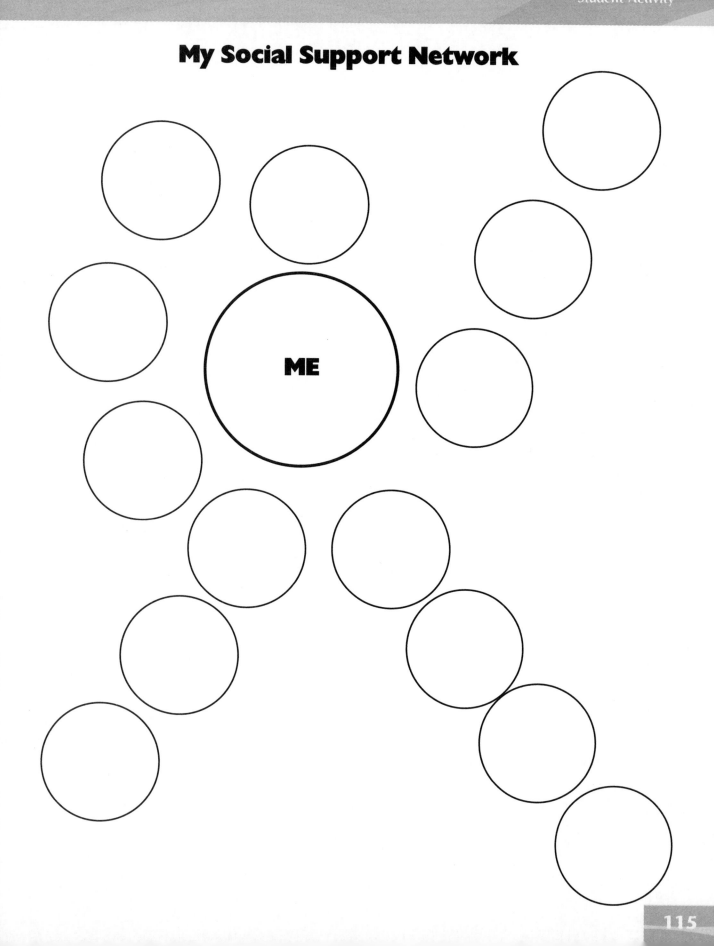

NAME:

Choosing for Health

Fill in the blanks. Write the word in the blank that best completes the sentence. Choose from the word bank. There are more words than you need in the bank.

Word Bank

nutrients endurance strength clean	heart rate lifestyle bone	flexibility physical fitness choices	muscle dreaming exercise

1. Your heart is a _____ . It needs _____ to beat strong.

2. During sleep, your _____ _____ slows down.

3. If you have muscle _____ , you are able to stretch and move easily.

4. Keeping your body _____ helps protect you from communicable diseases.

5. _____ _____ is an important part of a healthy lifestyle.

6. Muscle _____ helps a person lift, push, and pull objects without feeling tired.

7. If a person has _____ , he or she can exercise or play without tiring quickly.

8. A person who does not get enough _____ time is cranky and tired.

9. Eating right gives your body the _____ it needs.

10. You can make choices that help build a healthy _____ .

Short Essay. Answer the questions using complete sentences.

1. Why is serving God at the center of a healthy lifestyle? _____

    _____

    _____

    _____

2. How can other people help us be healthy? _____

    _____

    _____

    _____

3. Why do you eat what you do? Tell about two influences on your eating habits.

    _____

    _____

    _____

    _____

4. What does good personal health have to do with a healthy lifestyle? _____

    _____

    _____

    _____

    _____

NONRETURNABLE